Things to Make and Do for Girls

Published by Top That! Publishing plc
Tide Mill Way, Woodbridge, Suffolk, IP12 1AP, UK
www.topthatpublishing.com

KATY PILLAR

YOU WILL NEED:

- Three egg boxes
- Strong PVA glue
- Thin card
- Paint
- Paintbrushes
- Pencil
- Black marker pen
- Coloured card (red, yellow and green)
- Scissors

Three egg boxes form the different segments of this caterpillar's body and each of her eighteen feet wears little lace-up shoes! She's a cute creepy-crawly, and you can choose your favourite colours to decorate her body and bow. Dotty and spotty patterns look best, so get out your paintbrush and bring Katy the egg box caterpillar to life.

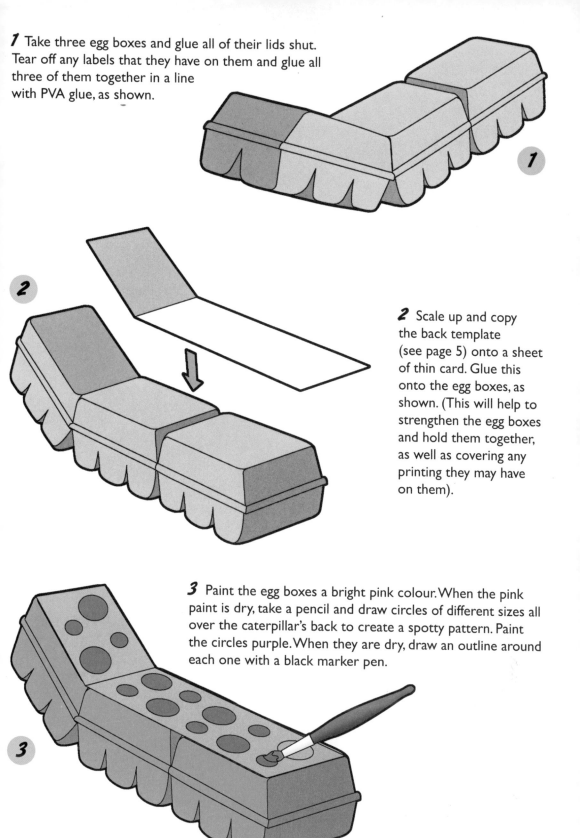

1 Take three egg boxes and glue all of their lids shut. Tear off any labels that they have on them and glue all three of them together in a line with PVA glue, as shown.

1

2

2 Scale up and copy the back template (see page 5) onto a sheet of thin card. Glue this onto the egg boxes, as shown. (This will help to strengthen the egg boxes and hold them together, as well as covering any printing they may have on them).

3 Paint the egg boxes a bright pink colour. When the pink paint is dry, take a pencil and draw circles of different sizes all over the caterpillar's back to create a spotty pattern. Paint the circles purple. When they are dry, draw an outline around each one with a black marker pen.

3

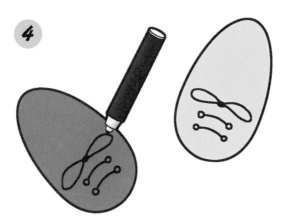

4

4 Scale up and copy the foot template provided (see page 5). Draw around this template ten times onto a piece of red card and eight times onto a piece of yellow card. Cut out all of the feet and add laces to them using a black marker pen.

5 Using PVA glue, stick the feet to the bottom of the egg boxes. Start at the front of the caterpillar with a pair of red feet, and then alternate between the two colours for each pair, as shown.

5

6 Scale up and copy the eyes, bow and tongue templates (see page 5) onto coloured card. Draw on details with a black marker pen and then glue them in place on the front of your caterpillar, as shown.

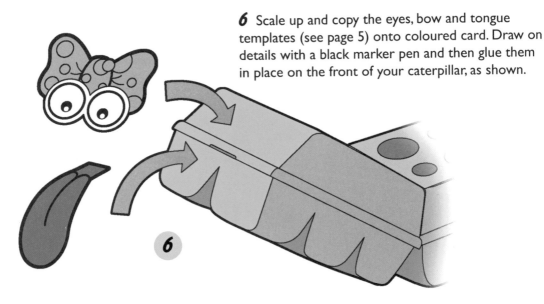

6

SCALING UP

The term **scale up** is referred to when you need to draw up the templates. This just means drawn up bigger than they appear on the page.

All the squares on the template page are equal to a 25 mm (1 in.) measurement, although on the page they appear smaller.
So you need to draw up a grid of squares that measure 25 mm (1 in.) on all sides, onto a piece of thick card. Then, using a pencil and ruler, carefully copy what you see on the template page into each square of your grid.

KATY PILLAR
TEMPLATES

Each square = 25 mm (1 in.) See above for instructions on how to scale up.

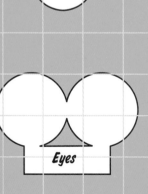

Tongue

Foot

Eyes

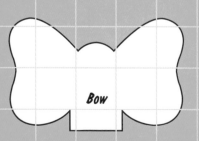

Bow

Back

FUZZY FLOWER

YOU WILL NEED:

- Fuzzy sticks (two pink, one green, half orange)
- Scissors

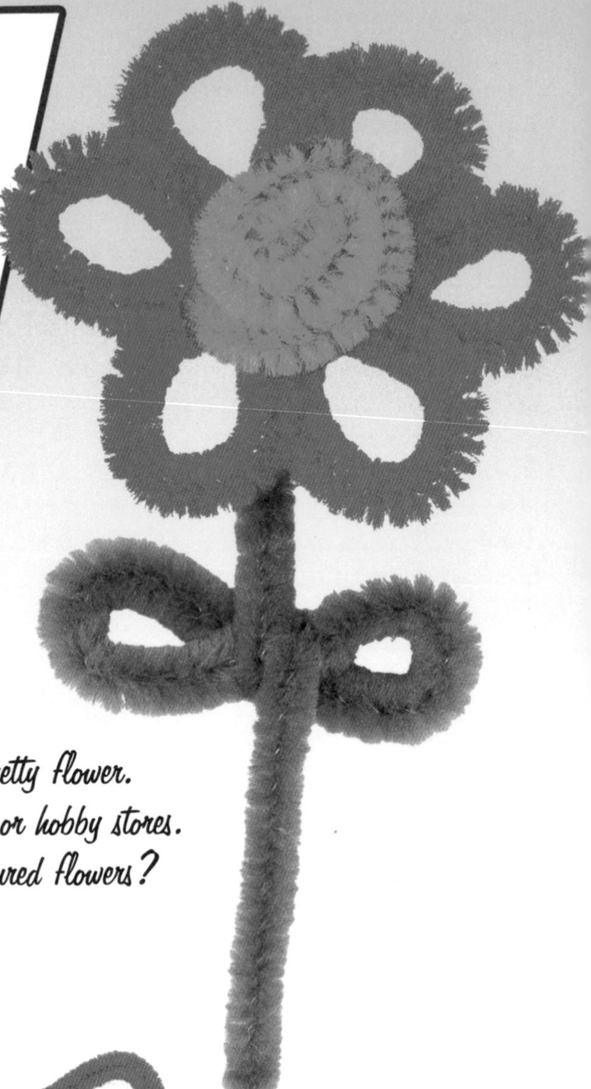

Set your fingers whizzing to create this pretty flower. You can buy fuzzy sticks from most craft or hobby stores. Why not try making lots of different coloured flowers?

1 Make a loop at one end of a pink stick and fold over the tip, as shown.

1

2 Make a second loop and twist the remaining stick around the tip.

2

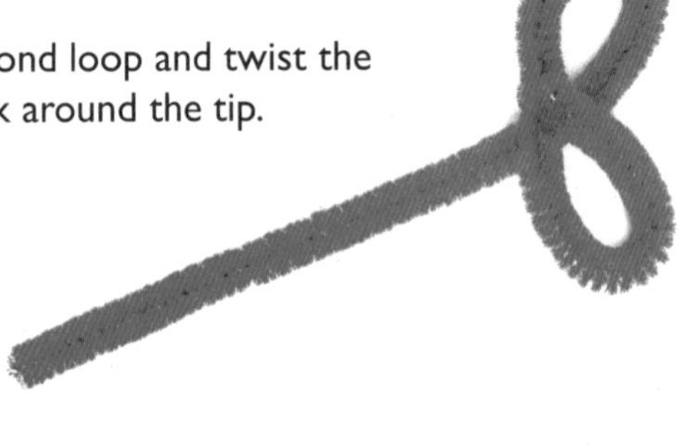

3

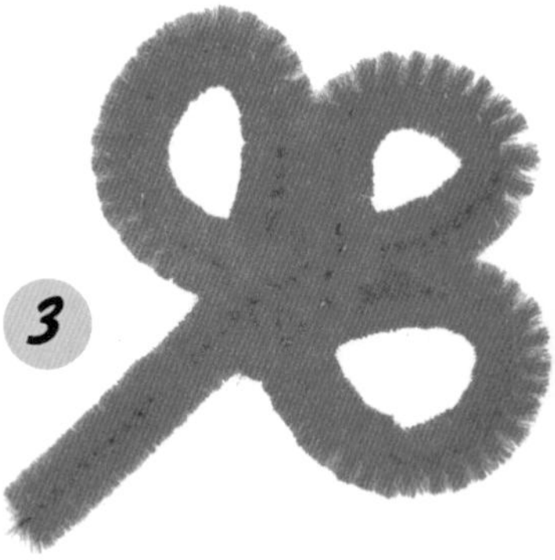

3 Make a third petal, twist the stick around the tip again and leave a stump.

4 Make another set of petals using the second pink stick, then join the two sets of petals together by twisting the stumps.

5 Make a swirl with the orange stick, leaving a 2 cm (3/4 in.) stump at the end.

6 Join the swirl to the petals by folding the 2 cm (3/4 in.) stump around the back of the petals.

7 Take the green fuzzy stick and cut it in half. Bend the stump of the orange swirl over to hold the green stem in place.

8 Make a 'figure of eight' with the remaining green stick and twist the ends together.

9 Wrap the stem around the centre of the leaves to hold them in place to finish.

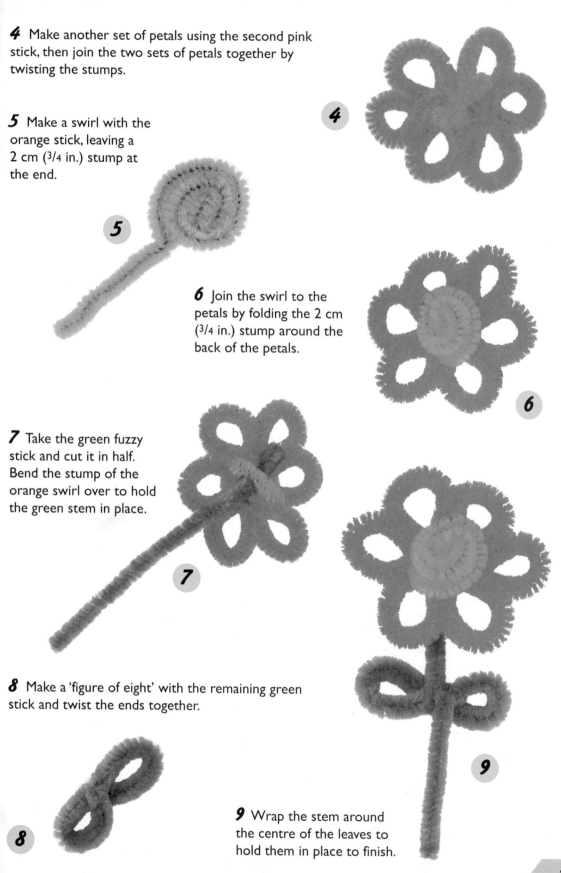

FRIENDSHIP BRACELET

One of the best things about making friendship bracelets is that you don't need many tools or materials. This fab bracelet is a great project to get you started!

1 Wrap a piece of string around the wrist of the person you are making the bracelet for. Cut the string so you know how long the bracelet needs to be.

2 Cut the threads you need to the right length and knot them together, leaving about 4 cm (1 1/2 in.) of loose thread at the end. Clip them to your weaving card (a clipboard, or a piece of cardboard with a bulldog clip at the top).

3 Knot the eight threads together at the top (we have used orange, red, yellow and white). On the weaving card, position the two white threads in the middle. Then place the other threads on either side of the central threads so that the colours mirror each other (orange on the outside, then red, then yellow).

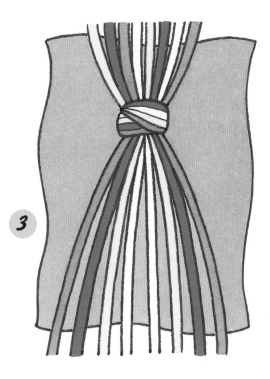

3

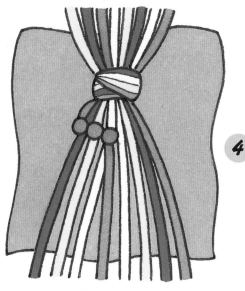

4

4 Use the left-hand thread to make left-loop full knots over the three threads next to it, and leave it in the middle.

5 Use the right-hand threads to make right-loop full knots into the middle. Knot the two orange threads together.

5

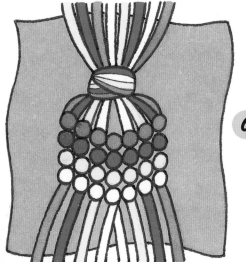

6

6 Continue knotting from left to centre then right to centre, and knotting in the middle, to make three more rows. The threads will now be back in the same order that you started with.

7 Use the left-hand thread to make two left-loop full knots over the next thread. Leave the left-hand thread on the outside. Use the right-hand thread to make two right-loop full knots over the next threads. Leave the right-hand thread on the outside.

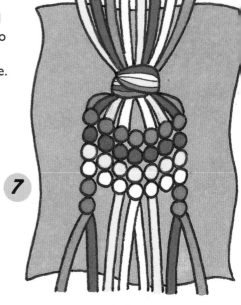

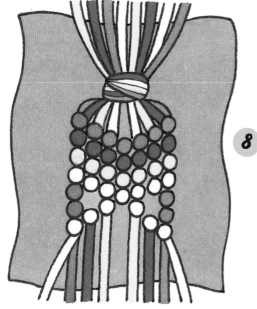

8 Move to the middle threads. Knot the right-middle thread over all the threads to the right using left-loop full knots. Knot the left-middle thread over all the threads to the left using right-loop full knots.

9 Knot the new middle threads together. Knot the right-middle thread over the next thread and the one after that, using left-loop full knots. Knot the left-middle thread over the next thread and the one after that, using right-loop full knots.

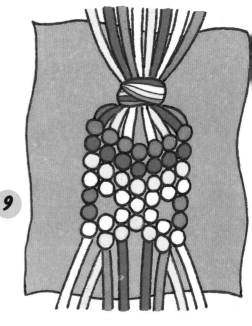

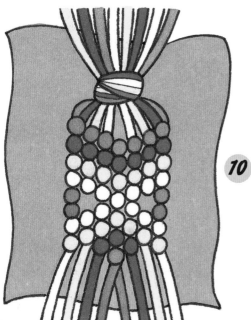

10 Knot the new middle threads together. Knot the right-middle thread over the next thread, using a left-loop full knot. Knot the left-middle thread over the next thread, using a right-loop full knot. Knot the new middle threads together.

11 Use the thread on the left of the middle threads to make a left-loop full knot over the left-middle thread next to it. Use the thread on the right of the middle threads to make a right-loop full knot over the right-middle thread next to it. Knot the new middle threads together.

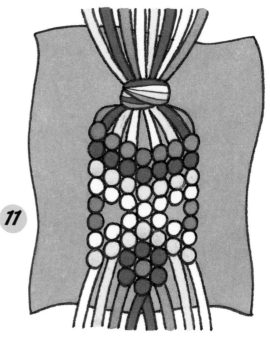

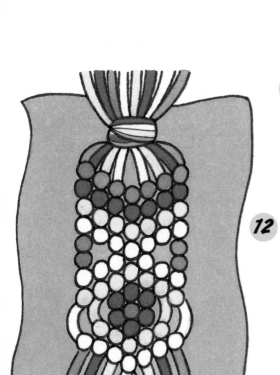

12 In the same way as in step 11, knot the threads third from the middle into the centre and knot them together. Then knot the outside threads into the middle and knot them together. The threads will now be in the order that you started with.

13 Keep following steps 4 to 12 until the bracelet is the same length as your measuring string.

14 Tie a knot to finish off the bracelet, and trim off any loose thread about 4 cm (1 1/2 in.) from the knot.

FAIRY FINGER PUPPET

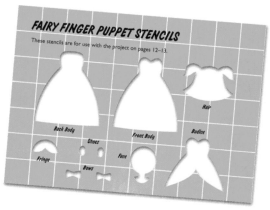

YOU WILL NEED:

Stencils from the stencil section

Pencil

Felt sheets (dark pink, pale pink, white and brown)

Scissors

Ribbon

Black & red pens

Glue

Glitter glue

Tinsel stick

This pretty fairy puppet is easy to make and fun to play with! Why not make some fairy friends for her to play with?

1 Find the 'Fairy Finger Puppet Stencils' in the stencil section.

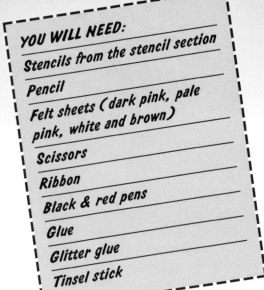

FAIRY FINGER PUPPET STENCILS

These stencils are for use with the project on pages 12–13.

Back Body   Front Body   Hair   Bodice   Shoes   Fringe   Face   Bows

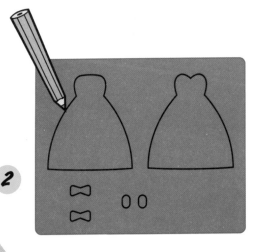

2 Using a pencil, carefully draw around the stencils onto the felt sheets (dark pink for the front body, back body, two shoes and two bows; pale pink for the face; white for the bodice; brown for the hair and fringe).

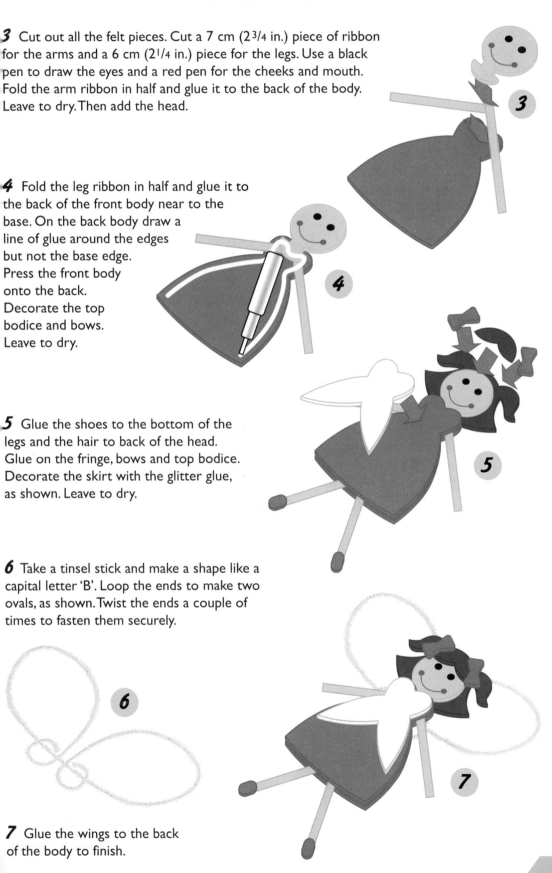

3 Cut out all the felt pieces. Cut a 7 cm (2 3/4 in.) piece of ribbon for the arms and a 6 cm (2 1/4 in.) piece for the legs. Use a black pen to draw the eyes and a red pen for the cheeks and mouth. Fold the arm ribbon in half and glue it to the back of the body. Leave to dry. Then add the head.

4 Fold the leg ribbon in half and glue it to the back of the front body near to the base. On the back body draw a line of glue around the edges but not the base edge. Press the front body onto the back. Decorate the top bodice and bows. Leave to dry.

5 Glue the shoes to the bottom of the legs and the hair to back of the head. Glue on the fringe, bows and top bodice. Decorate the skirt with the glitter glue, as shown. Leave to dry.

6 Take a tinsel stick and make a shape like a capital letter 'B'. Loop the ends to make two ovals, as shown. Twist the ends a couple of times to fasten them securely.

7 Glue the wings to the back of the body to finish.

VALENTINE CUPCAKES

! ADULT HELP NEEDED

YOU WILL NEED:

Bun case baking tray

Paper cases

Mixing bowl

Sieve

Wooden spoon

Wire rack

125 g (4 1/2 oz) margarine

125 g (4 1/2 oz) self-raising flour

125 g (4 1/2 oz) caster sugar

2 eggs

2-3 tablespoons milk

Fresh whipped cream

Desiccated coconut

Share these muffins with the people that you love. They make great presents or just have fun baking them and enjoy them yourself!

1 Put paper cases in the bun case baking tray. Preheat the oven to 200°C / 390°F / gas mark 6.

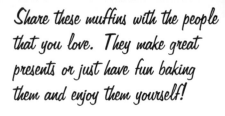

2 Put the margarine into a bowl then sift the flour over the top.

3 Use the tips of your fingers to rub the margarine and flour together until the mixture becomes crumbly.

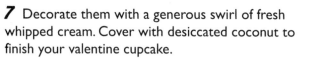

4 Add the sugar and stir in the eggs. Finally, add enough milk to make the mixture creamy.

5 Put spoonfuls of the mixture into the paper cases.

6 Bake the cupcakes for 10–15 minutes, then leave them to cool on a wire rack.

7 Decorate them with a generous swirl of fresh whipped cream. Cover with desiccated coconut to finish your valentine cupcake.

DESIGNER APPLIQUÉ

WARNING!

Needles are very sharp and should be handled with great care.

Do not attempt to make any of the designer appliqué projects until you are confident using a needle. You will need adult supervision, so remember to ask for help before you begin.

Appliqué is a fun hobby that you can do anywhere. It is an art that uses all kinds of materials and styles of needlework. You and your friends will have great fun learning the art of appliqué and making these really cool projects. Then design some of your own using the cool stitches and techniques that you have learnt. Keep your eyes open for ribbons, beads, pretty trimmings, sequins, threads and fabric scraps.

Before you begin the projects, practise some of the stitches on a piece of scrap fabric. Experiment with different colour combinations and choose colours that work with the item you are decorating.

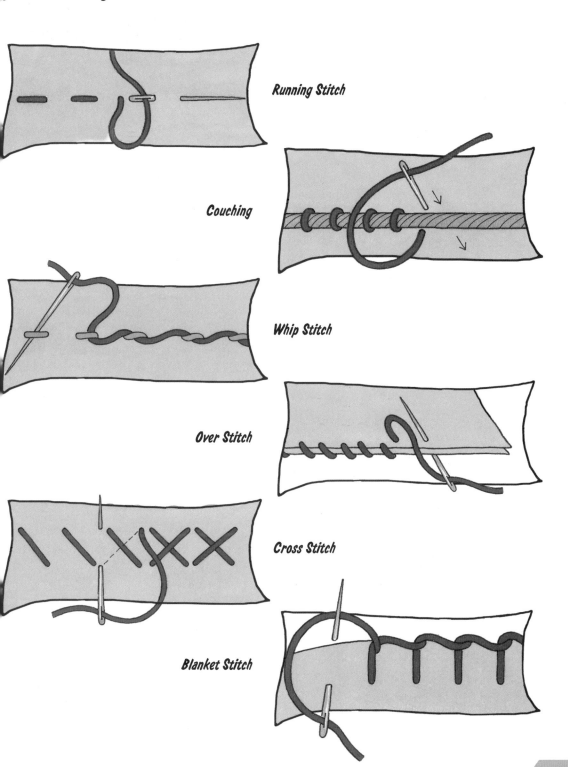

Running Stitch

Couching

Whip Stitch

Over Stitch

Cross Stitch

Blanket Stitch

NOTEBOOK COVER

Once you have learnt the simple stitches on page 17, you will be able to design and create beautiful projects of your own.

This great notebook cover is fun and easy to make, and once you get the hang of it, you'll be able to make covers for everything, including books, pencil cases and folders!

1 First, measure the front of your notebook that you are covering, then cut out two pieces of denim fabric that are slightly bigger than the notebook. Place one piece of fabric onto your work surface face down. Next lay the notebook on top of the fabric and draw around the four sides. This is the area that you will work inside.

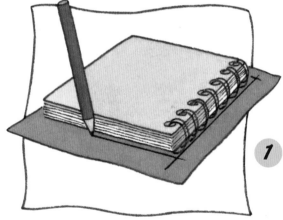

2 Draw a star shape onto a piece of paper and cut it out. Using this template, draw the shape onto a piece of yellow felt, then cut it out. Sew the star onto one of the pieces of denim using a running stitch and turquoise thread.

3 Now using pink thread, sew five rows of stitching from the centre of the star out towards each point.

3

4 Decorate the space around the centre star with small stitched stars in three different colours. Each star is simply made up of three large stitches criss-crossing over each other. Start and finish each star with an over stitch on the back of the piece of material.

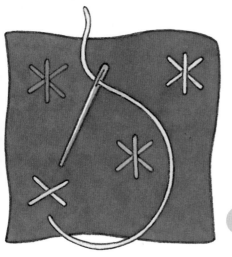

4

5 Glue the decorated piece of denim onto the front cover of the notebook. Glue the second piece of denim fabric onto the inside front cover of the notebook. Leave to dry.

6 Now sew along the three outside edges of the notebook through both pieces of denim material. Use whip stitching and yellow and pink thread.

6

7 Finally, fray the denim edges then cut them straight so they look neat.

KEYRING

YOU WILL NEED:

Thin paper

Pencil

Scissors

Orange felt 5 cm x 14 cm
(2 in. x 5 1/2 in.)

Pins

Yellow felt 3.5 cm x 3.5 cm
(1 1/4 in. x 1 1/4 in.)

Lime felt 3.5 cm x 3.5 cm
(1 1/4 in. x 1 1/4 in.)

Embroidery needle

Embroidery thread
(orange, lime, yellow)

1 orange bead

1 lime seed bead

Keyring loop

You'll never lose your keys again with this great keyring design! We have used orange, lime and yellow, but feel free to use your favourite colours. They make fantastic presents too so why not make more for your friends and family? What are you waiting for ... get started!

1 On a piece of paper draw a keyring shape, then cut it out. Now fold the orange felt in half and pin the template to it. Carefully cut around the template, making sure you cut through both sides of the doubled up fabric.

1

2

2 Draw a flower and square shape onto a piece of paper, and then cut them out to make your templates. Pin the flower template onto the yellow felt and the square template onto the lime felt and carefully cut around each one. Lay the flower shape onto the lime felt square and stitch it in place using a running stitch and orange thread.

3 Now place the lime square on one side of the orange felt and sew around the outside using small over stitches and yellow thread.

3

4

4 Again using yellow thread, sew through the centre of the flower, from back to front. Now thread an orange bead followed by a lime seed bead onto the yellow thread. Take the needle back through the orange bead and through to the back of the fabric. Secure with an over stitch on the back of the fabric.

5

5 Finally, thread the keyring loop onto the orange felt shape. Now fold the felt in half, and then sew the two layers together using a blanket stitch and lime thread.

GIFT BOX

YOU WILL NEED:

Small round gift box with lid
(approximately 7 cm
(2 3/4 in.) diameter)

Pencil

Scissors

Green paint

Paintbrush

Varnish (optional)

Needle

Nylon monofilament

84 green seed beads

8 flower shaped beads

5 larger green beads

Glue

16 clear seed beads

Gift box stickers from the
sticker section (optional)

This beautiful box makes a brilliant gift even when its empty!

1 Take the lid and draw a circle in its centre, about 1.5 cm (1/2 in.) from the edge. Cut out the circle to leave a hole.

2 Paint the box and the lid with green paint. It may need two coats. When the paint is dry you can varnish the box if you wish to.

3 Make four pencil marks 5 mm (1/5 in.) apart, about 3 mm (1/8 in.) from the edge of the hole. On the opposite side of the hole make four more marks. Make a further two sets of marks between the first ones.

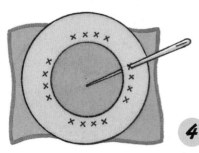

4 Ask an adult to carefully use a needle to punch a hole through the box where you have made each mark.

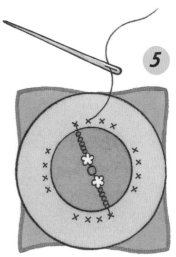

5 Cut a 1 m (39 in.) length of monofilament. Tie one end securely through the first hole in one of the sets of four. Thread on 5 green seed beads, 1 flower bead, 1 large green bead, 1 flower bead and 5 green seed beads. Take the thread diagonally across the box and through the first hole on the opposite side. Wrap it around once then thread it through the next hole and wrap it once again.

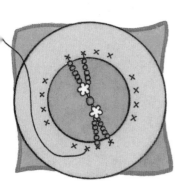

6 Thread on five seed beads. Take the thread through the large green bead. Thread on five seed beads and then take the thread diagonally across the box and through the next hole on the opposite side. Wrap the thread and move on to the next hole as before. Repeat this step.

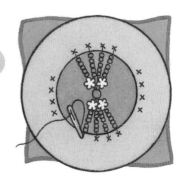

7 Thread on five green seed beads, and a flower bead. Take the thread through the large green bead. Thread on a flower bead, and five green seed beads. Wrap the thread once around the fourth hole.

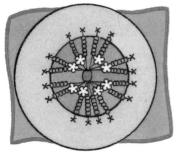

8 Now take the thread across to the next set of holes. Repeat step 7, then repeat step 6 twice. Finally repeat step 7. Secure the thread tightly with a knot. Trim away excess thread.

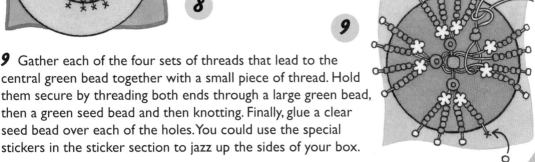

9 Gather each of the four sets of threads that lead to the central green bead together with a small piece of thread. Hold them secure by threading both ends through a large green bead, then a green seed bead and then knotting. Finally, glue a clear seed bead over each of the holes. You could use the special stickers in the sticker section to jazz up the sides of your box.

ICE CREAM SUNDAE

YOU WILL NEED:
- 100 g (4 oz) strawberries
- 25 g (1 oz) icing sugar
- 1 teaspoon water
- 4 scoops strawberry ice cream
- 75 ml (3 fl. oz) whipped cream, to decorate
- Glacé cherries, to decorate

This fab fruity sundae is great as an after-school treat!

EQUIPMENT YOU WILL NEED:
- Blender
- Sieve
- Sundae glass
- Piping bag

1 Ask an adult to purée half of the strawberries in a blender with the icing sugar and 1 teaspoon of water.

2 Then, carefully push the purée through a sieve to remove the seeds.

3 Pour a small amount of purée into the bottom of a sundae glass, then follow by piling a scoop of strawberry ice cream and a tablespoon of whipped cream. Repeat the process.

4 Place the remaining whipped cream into a piping bag and pipe it onto the top of the sundae. Top with a whole strawberry or glacé cherry to finish.

CITRUS LOLLIES

There will be bursts of yummy flavours in these citrus lollies!

1 Pour the first cordial into the ice lolly moulds, along with a splash of water, until each mould is about half full. Place the moulds into the freezer and leave them to set for at least 4 hours, until solid.

1

2 Repeat the process, but this time with the different-flavoured cordial. Pour on top of the frozen layer and place into the freezer, until solid.

2

3

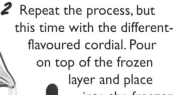

3 Remove the lollies from the moulds and enjoy!

HEARTS & STARS STATIONERY

YOU WILL NEED:

Hearts & stars stencils from the stencil section

Pencil

Piece of paper

White or pale coloured PVC stationery

Fine black marker pen

Acrylic paint (pink and yellow)

Paintbrush

You'll be the envy of all your friends with this gorgeous stationery!

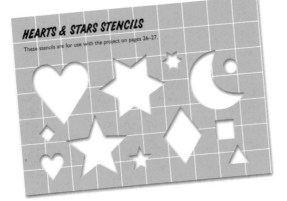

HEARTS & STARS STENCILS

These stencils are for use with the project on pages 26–27.

1 Find the 'Hearts and Stars Stencils' in the stencil section.

1

2 Using a pencil, carefully draw around the stencils onto a piece of paper the size of your piece of stationery. Choose your favourite shapes, evenly covering the paper with hearts and stars.

3 Place the piece of paper underneath the PVC stationery. Now carefully follow the design, outlining the shapes onto the stationery with a fine black marker pen.

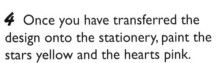

4 Once you have transferred the design onto the stationery, paint the stars yellow and the hearts pink.

5 Leave to dry, flat if possible, although some nice effects can be created if the paint runs slightly and the surface is uneven.

6 Now decorate other pieces of stationery with hearts and stars to match.

MOSAIC PICTURE FRAME

This colourful picture frame will make a great addition to any home!

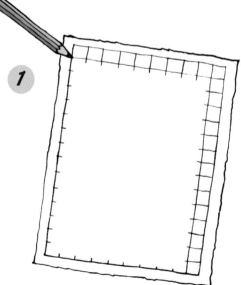

1 Lay the glass front of the frame on a piece of paper and draw around it. Make marks at 1 cm (1/4 in.) intervals along the top, bottom and sides of the rectangle you have drawn. Join the marks with straight lines, from top to bottom and side to side. This will form a grid.

2 Rub out the centre section of the grid, leaving a rectangle large enough to display a photograph. Lay the drawing underneath the glass front once more. This will be the template for your mosaic.

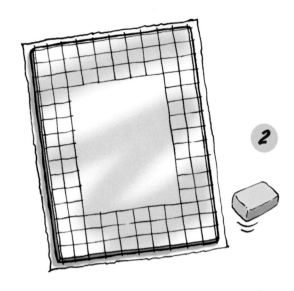

3 Take one of the coloured paints and carefully start to colour in the first square on the top row. Do not paint right up to the edge as a tiny border will give the frame a mosaic look when complete. Wash the brush then use a different colour to paint the next square. Continue across the frame, changing the colour for each square.

4 Work on the next row of squares. Make sure that the colour you use is different from the square above and next to it. Continue to fill in all of the squares until you reach the bottom of the frame.

5 Once the paint has dried, turn the glass over and lay it painted side down over your chosen picture. This will stop the paint from being marked when you clip the frame back together.

SCHOOL STUFF

PENCIL TIN & NOTEBOOK
YOU WILL NEED:

Plain metal pencil tin

Masking tape

Paint

Paintbrush

Paw print stencils from the stencil section

Sticky label

Plain notebook

Stencils brighten up the most boring of objects, and it's so easy! Try out the stencils included on some of your school stuff.

FOLDER
YOU WILL NEED:

A4 ringbinder

Sticky label

Stencils from the stencil section

Masking tape

Paint

Paintbrush

PENCIL TIN & NOTEBOOK

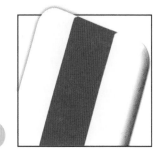

1 Lay masking tape along either side of the top of the pencil tin lid, leaving a gap of 4 cm (1 1/2 in.) between the two strips.

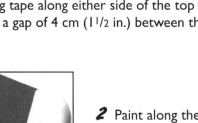

2 Paint along the gap between the strips with a bright colour. You can be as messy as you want as the tape protects the rest of the tin! When the paint has dried, peel off the tape.

3 Stencil the paw print design along the length of the tin with black paint. To complete the set, stencil a paw print onto a sticky label and attach to the notebook.

FOLDER

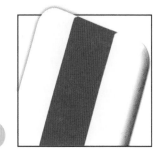

1 Stick a label in the centre of the folder. Position the cat stencil so it just touches the left-hand side of the label and attach with masking tape. Fill in the cat with red paint.

2 Lift off the stencil, and leave it to dry. Then, turn it over so that the cat faces the other way. Position it onto the right-hand side of the label, secure with masking tape and paint the cat again.

3 Position the paw print stencil at the bottom right-hand corner of the folder. Fill it in with black paint and leave to dry. Repeat the design, following the pattern shown opposite.

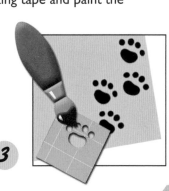

DECORATED HAIRBAND

⚠️ ADULT HELP NEEDED

YOU WILL NEED:

Hairband

Beading needle

Cotton

Seed beads (orange, white)

Jazz up some plain hair accessories with this fun idea.

1 Stitch in and out of the band on the same spot to secure the thread. Thread five orange beads onto the cotton. Pull them in a diagonal direction, top to bottom, then stitch in and out of the band again.

2 Now thread on five white beads, but this time pull them in a diagonal direction from bottom to top.

3 Once again, stitch in and out of the band. Repeat this threading pattern, forming a zig-zag of white and orange beads along your hairband.

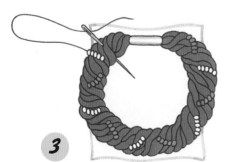

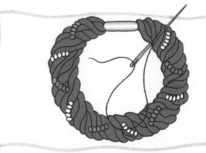

4 Secure the end with a few stitches on the same spot, and trim away any threads.

PAPIER MÂCHÉ LETTERS

YOU WILL NEED:

- Bowl
- Wallpaper paste
- Spoon
- Newspaper
- Card or old cloth
- Poster paints

Just let your imagination run wild with these papier mâché letters! If you have any papier mâché mix left, cover it with plastic film until you are ready to use it again — it should last for three to four days.

1 Mix the wallpaper paste with water following the pack instructions.

2 Tear up lots of small strips of old newspaper and stir them into the paste. Keep adding newspaper strips until your mixture is thick.

3 Cover your work surface with a piece of card or old cloth. Then, using small lumps of papier mâché, layer and mould your letters. Leave the letters to dry overnight.

4 When your letters are completely dry, they are ready to be decorated. Paint them in bright colours, cover them in spots or get creative with lines and swirls. Once the letters have dried, you can use them to make posters, greeting cards or a name plaque for your room.

NAIL ART

YOU WILL NEED:

Nail varnish

Fine paintbrush

Cocktail stick

Nail art stencils from the stencil section

It's time to give your hands a stylish makeover! Try out some of these tips and then release your creative side!

TOP TIPS FOR BEAUTIFUL NAILS!

1 Keep your nails healthy and strong by soaking them in a bowl of olive oil. Do this once a week for about five minutes, rinse them and then rub in lots of hand cream.

2 Never file your nails backwards and forwards across the top. Only file in one direction, working from the left to the centre then the right to the centre.

3 Don't file your nails after they have been wet. They are much stronger when they're properly dry.

4 Dark nail polish will stain your nails, so always use a clear undercoat before painting them.

5 Don't forget your toenails! They need as much love and attention as your fingernails. Cut the nails straight across to avoid ingrowing toenails, and don't shape the edges.

THE BASE COAT

Learn to paint a smooth base coat on your nails,
and your designs will look much better.

1 Remove most of the varnish from your brush. Wipe it carefully against the inside of the bottle rim so it can drip back into the bottle. Don't let it drip outside, or your bottle will seal up before the varnish is all gone!

2 Partially dip the brush back into the varnish to pick up just a small amount of colour. Paint a single, firm stroke up the centre of your nail, from base to tip.

3 Complete your nail with another single stroke on each side. Now dip your brush into the varnish ready for the next nail.

PAINTING TIPS

Regular brushes that come with nail varnish are too big for painting fine details. It's easier to use a very fine paintbrush and a cocktail stick.

Dip the tip of your brush into the colour and dab a circle of varnish onto the nail where you need it. Shape it by dragging the paintbrush or a cocktail stick through the circle. Add tiny details with the point of the stick. Always leave one colour to dry before adding the next.

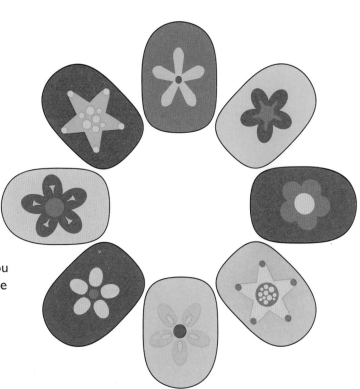

STRIPES

1 Paint a single colour onto all of your nails and let them dry. Use bright colours if you're feeling bold!

2 Use a thin brush to make a single, neat stroke for either of these stripes. Start at the base of the nail and pull the brush upwards.

3 Horizontal stripes are more tricky. Start at one side and pull the brush across the nail. To add a third colour, wait until the second is totally dry.

CHECKS

1 Paint a base coat and let it dry.

2 Add stripes in one colour, slanting across the nail.

3 When the first stripes are dry, paint a second set over the top, going in the opposite direction.

Why not go mad with lots of different colours to create a chic nail art design that any catwalk model would be proud to wear!

DOTS

1 Paint a base coat and let it dry.

2 Paint bright coloured dots all over your nail.

3 Add coloured centres using a cocktail stick!

Or make stripes out of a diagonal row of tiny dots, using the point of a cocktail stick. Let the first colour dry and then add more dots in a second colour!

STENCILS

A number of different stencils can be found in your stencil section. Experiment to see which designs you like the best!

1 Paint a base coat on your nails and leave them to dry.

2 To use the stencils, choose your pattern and position the hole on your nail. Carefully dab a different colour over the hole before lifting off the stencil.

3 Allow the shapes to dry, then add fine features with a cocktail stick.

SYMBOLS

Simple symbols look really effective if you use your most sparkly nail varnish!

Paint a single base colour on all of your nails, then use a different colour for the patterns.

CHRISTMAS NAILS

Make your own stencils to create these fun festive designs. Perfect for the Christmas party season!

Finish off your designs with painted details using a paintbrush and cocktail stick.

HEART-SHAPED KEYRING

ADULT HELP NEEDED

YOU WILL NEED:

Thin wire approximately 1 m (39 in.)

Assorted pink and purple beads

White seed beads

Keyring chain

Small pliers

Keep your keys together with this stylish keyring.

1 Starting at one end, bend the wire into a small heart about 5 cm (2 in.) high. Twist the ends together to secure the heart-shaped frame, leaving one long wire length.

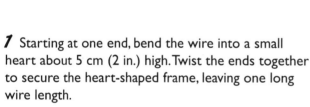

1

2 Thread some beads onto the wire in a random sequence, then pull it over to any point on the heart frame and attach it by winding it once around the wire frame.

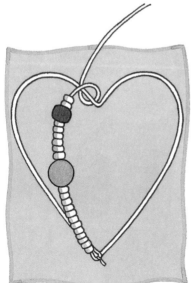

2

3 Repeat step 2 using a different combination of beads each time, and crisscross the wires to create a mesh of wire and beads.

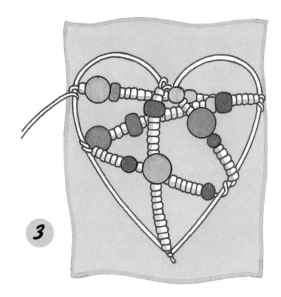

4 When the heart frame is full of beads, trim away the excess wire, leaving enough to wrap around the frame to secure in position, ensuring there are no sharp edges.

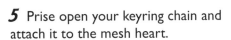

5 Prise open your keyring chain and attach it to the mesh heart.

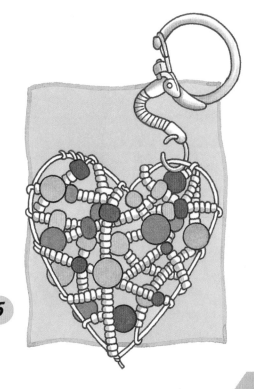

CRAZY COOKIES

**COOKIE INGREDIENTS
YOU WILL NEED:**

100g (4 oz) butter
or soft margarine

100g (4 oz) caster sugar

1 egg

200 g (8 oz) plain flour

*Let your imagination run wild when decorating these crazy cookies,
but watch out that you don't make them too good to eat!*

**EQUIPMENT
YOU WILL NEED:**

Baking trays

Large bowl

Wooden spoon

Sieve

Rolling pin

Cookie cutters

Palette knife

Wire rack

Small bowls

Icing syringe

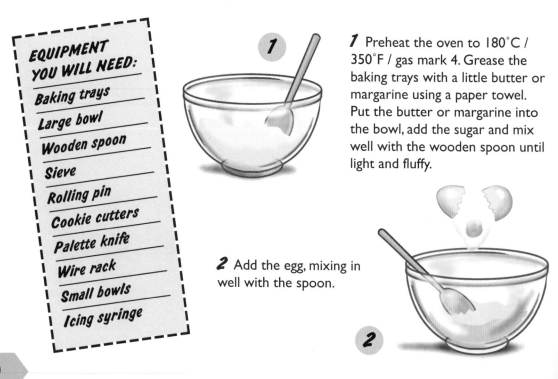

1 Preheat the oven to 180°C /
350°F / gas mark 4. Grease the
baking trays with a little butter or
margarine using a paper towel.
Put the butter or margarine into
the bowl, add the sugar and mix
well with the wooden spoon until
light and fluffy.

2 Add the egg, mixing in
well with the spoon.

3 Pour flour into the sieve over the bowl and sift into the mixture. Gently mix in the flour. Using your hands, knead the mixture into a smooth dough. Put into the fridge for 15 minutes.

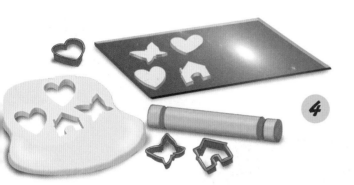

4 Put the dough onto a floured surface, sprinkle a little flour onto the rolling pin, and roll out the dough, not too thin. Use the cutters to cut out the biscuits and put onto the baking tray using the palette knife. Bake in the oven for 10 minutes until golden brown. Lift onto the wire rack to cool before decorating.

**WATER ICING
YOU WILL NEED:**

100 g (4 oz)
icing sugar

1-2 tablespoons water

Food colouring (optional)

1 teaspoon cocoa powder
(optional)

Water icing Sift the icing sugar into a bowl and add enough water to make a thick smooth paste, using a wooden spoon. Add one or two drops of food colouring. To make chocolate icing, add one teaspoon of cocoa powder to the icing sugar before sifting.

**ROYAL ICING
YOU WILL NEED:**

1 egg white

100 g (4 oz)
icing sugar

Food colouring
(optional)

Royal icing
Put an egg white into a small bowl and beat lightly with a fork. Sift the icing sugar into another bowl, add the egg white and beat well until the icing thickens. Add a drop of food colouring if you wish, to make the icing a colour of your choice.

TUMBLING BUTTERFLY

This acrobatic flier gracefully tumbles as it flies through the air. Make your flier look extra special by decorating it with a design like the one shown above, or create your own design.

1 Push out the die-cut from the project component section and place it, or a square sheet of paper, design-side down. Fold in half from right to left, as shown, making sure the black triangle is pointing right (if using the die-cut).

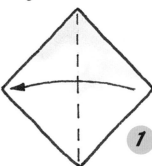

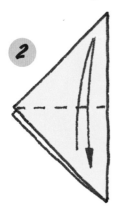

2 Fold and unfold in half from bottom to top. (This is called a valley fold).

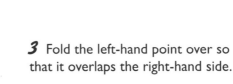

3 Fold the left-hand point over so that it overlaps the right-hand side.

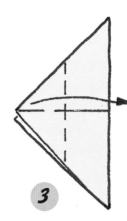

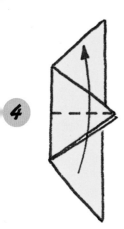

4 Now fold in half from bottom to top.

NO BOYS ALLOWED!

5 Fold the front flap forwards and the back flap behind, making the Tumbling Butterfly wings.

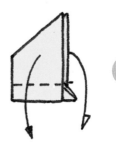

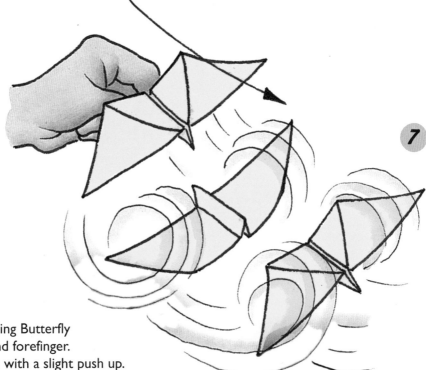

6 Lift the wings up so that they are horizontal. Open them out a little, as shown. This completes the Tumbling Butterfly.

7 Hold the Tumbling Butterfly between thumb and forefinger. Throw it forwards with a slight push up. As it falls, it will gracefully tumble over and over.

DECORATED TRINKET POTS

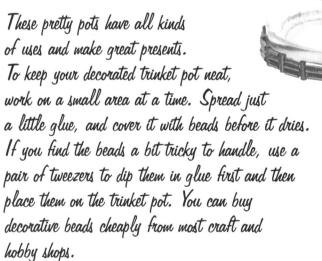

These pretty pots have all kinds
of uses and make great presents.
To keep your decorated trinket pot neat,
work on a small area at a time. Spread just
a little glue, and cover it with beads before it dries.
If you find the beads a bit tricky to handle, use a
pair of tweezers to dip them in glue first and then
place them on the trinket pot. You can buy
decorative beads cheaply from most craft and
hobby shops.

1 Working around the top of the pot, stick three
red bugle beads vertically, followed by three
horizontal blue bugle beads.

1

2 Repeat this pattern, working around the rim of the pot. If the pattern doesn't fit exactly, don't worry, simply fill the space with more red or blue beads. Leave to dry.

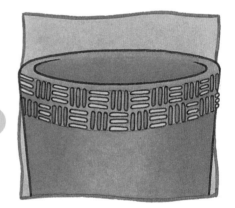

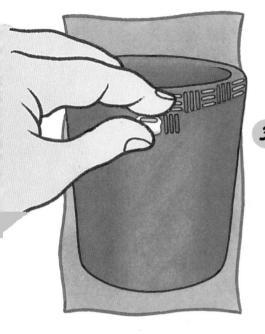

3 Work another row of beads underneath the first. Stick three red vertical bugle beads directly underneath three blue horizontal beads on the first row. Next stick three blue horizontal bugle beads next to them, directly below three red vertical beads.

4 Continue working around the pot until the rim is complete. You can then put beads around the base of the pot if you wish. Leave to dry.

Simple heart design This design is just as easy. Stick the heart-shaped beads and seed beads alternately around the middle of the trinket pot. Continue working around the pot. Leave to dry.

f you are planning to use your trinket pot to hold pens and pencils, and don't plan to wash it, then you could use the pretty stickers from the sticker section to add even more decorations.

MAKE YOUR OWN GIFT-WRAP

YOU WILL NEED:

Card

Paper

Masking tape

Pencils

Crayons

Gift-wrap stencils from the stencil section

Gift-wrap labels from the sticker section

Design your own wrapping paper using stencilled letters. You could write a message like 'Happy Birthday', or the name of the person you are making the paper for.

1 Find the 'Gift-wrap Stencils' in the stencil section.

2 Place your stencil over a piece of paper, then scribble all over the letter shapes. You may like to use some masking tape to hold the edges of your stencil down so that it doesn't move about while you are scribbling over it.

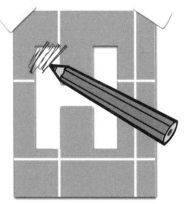

3 Remove the stencil, and your letters will now be on the piece of paper underneath. Use paints or chalks to achieve different effects. Add a label using the stickers in the sticker section to complete your personalised gift-wrap.

PRINTING LETTERS

ADULT HELP NEEDED

Here's a simple printing technique which you can do, using potatoes. Use different-sized potatoes and a selection of colours to achieve a wide variety of effects. Cutting out a letter 'H' to print is easy, but other letters are a bit more tricky — remember, always cut your letters out back to front so that they print the right way round.

1 Cut the top off the potato.

1

2 Now cut off the edges of the potato half-way down, so that you are left with a rectangular block.

2

3 Cut a letter from the rectangular block.

3

4 Dry the top of the letter, then dip it face down into the paint. Make sure it has a good, even coating.

4

5 Gently press your potato letter onto the card, then lift it off to reveal your printed letter.

5

PRACTICAL JOKES

Everyone loves to laugh and these practical jokes will have your friends and family in stitches. Before you start, here are a few hints and tips on how to be the world's number one joker, and ensure that your chosen dupe enjoys the prank as well.

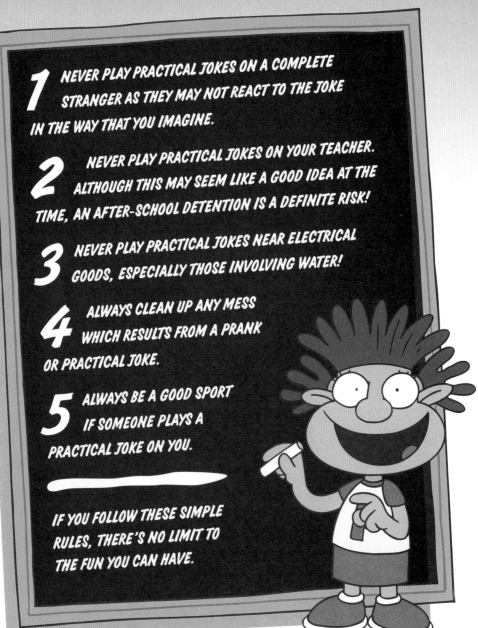

1 NEVER PLAY PRACTICAL JOKES ON A COMPLETE STRANGER AS THEY MAY NOT REACT TO THE JOKE IN THE WAY THAT YOU IMAGINE.

2 NEVER PLAY PRACTICAL JOKES ON YOUR TEACHER. ALTHOUGH THIS MAY SEEM LIKE A GOOD IDEA AT THE TIME, AN AFTER-SCHOOL DETENTION IS A DEFINITE RISK!

3 NEVER PLAY PRACTICAL JOKES NEAR ELECTRICAL GOODS, ESPECIALLY THOSE INVOLVING WATER!

4 ALWAYS CLEAN UP ANY MESS WHICH RESULTS FROM A PRANK OR PRACTICAL JOKE.

5 ALWAYS BE A GOOD SPORT IF SOMEONE PLAYS A PRACTICAL JOKE ON YOU.

IF YOU FOLLOW THESE SIMPLE RULES, THERE'S NO LIMIT TO THE FUN YOU CAN HAVE.

COIN CHUCKLES

This trick works best if your victim follows your instructions word for word. Make sure to do this trick just before the person is going outside so lots of people get to see your victim's new make-up!

1 Ask your victim if they're brave enough to take part in a world-famous co-ordination test. Tell them that the object of the test is to see if both halves of their brain are co-ordinated.

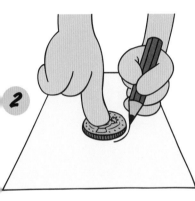

2 Ask your victim to place a coin on a piece of paper. Then get them to put their finger on the coin and draw round it with a pencil. Tell them to keep their finger on the coin at all times.

3 Ask your victim to repeat this exercise using each finger of both hands. When they've finished they should have drawn ten circles on their piece of paper and be looking as pleased as a wombat on holiday (pretty pleased).

4 Now comes the devious trickster bit. Tell them that to see if both halves of their brain are co-ordinated, they have to run the edge of the coin down the centre of their face.

5 If they can't do it, then they have failed the test. Of course, everyone can do it, but as you'll see, when they do it they get a big black line down their face! Ha! Ha!

PANTS PRANK

YOU WILL NEED:

Needle

Thread

Adult permission

This practical joke is a big pile of pants.
If your dad is one of those people who's always in a hurry
then this will work even better. Ask your mum to help you
with the sewing, it's a well known fact that mums are some of
the best jokers in the world!

1 Make sure your dad's not around and sneak into his bedroom.

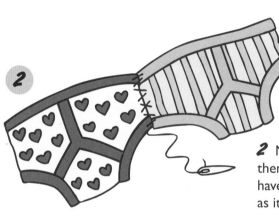

2 Now take two pairs of his pants and sew them together along one of the edges. It doesn't have to be the best sewing in the world as long as it holds the pants together.

3 Keep sewing the pants together along their edges to make a big chain of pants.

4 Once you've completed your chain of pants, carefully place them all back in the drawer, making sure that they look normal. When your dad next goes to pull out some underwear he'll get a lot more underwear than he bargained for! If he gets a bit cold he can always wear them as a scarf!

NICE TO SNOW YOU!

YOU WILL NEED:

Paper

Hole punch

Cardboard box

Scissors

Stickers from the sticker section

In the world of the prankster, it doesn't have to be winter for it to snow, at least not on your unsuspecting victim. A word of warning — don't try this on polar bears as they can get quite cross when they find out it's not real snow, only little bits of paper.

1 First of all you have to make your snow. Punch lots of holes out of the paper and collect the hole bits that collect in the bottom. Remember – the more the merrier!

1

2 Now take your cardboard box and carefully cut a hole in the bottom.

2

3 Place the box somewhere your victim will see it, try and put it somewhere above head height if you can and make it tempting so they won't be able to resist looking in it. The 'Nice to Snow You' stickers from the sticker section will make the box look more exciting!

3

4 Fill the box with the paper snow while it is on the shelf, with the hole resting on the shelf, so none can fall out.

4

5 When your victim spots the box they'll have to lift it down to see what it is. They'll find themselves covered in fake snow – vacuum cleaners at the ready before it melts!

5

BALLOON MOUSE

YOU WILL NEED:

One long modelling balloon

A black marker pen (optional)

Stickers from the sticker section

Some very small bubbles make up this little balloon character. You will need to squeeze the air out of some of them before you twist, so that they are only half as fat as the main balloon.

1 Begin with a long balloon inflated to just 20 cm (8 in.). Squeeze and twist a 5 cm (2 in.) bubble for the head.

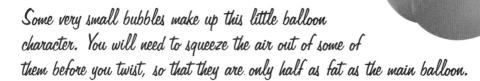

2 Squeeze and twist a 3 cm (1¹⁄4 in.) bubble and then twist it to the head.

3 Squeeze and twist another 3 cm (1¹⁄4 in.) bubble. Then twist it next to the first. Hold the balloon knot and tug it down and round to make the head bubble curve and look more mouse-like.

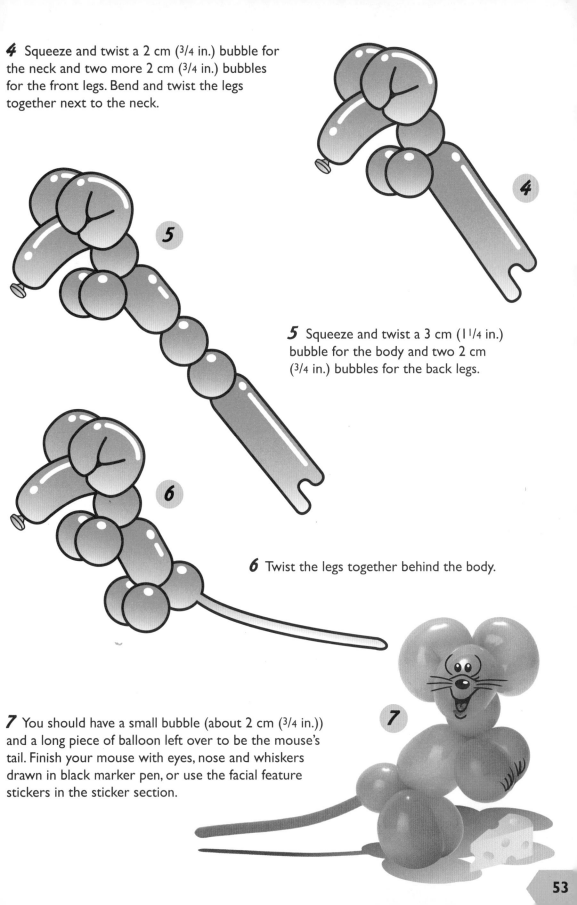

4 Squeeze and twist a 2 cm (³/4 in.) bubble for the neck and two more 2 cm (³/4 in.) bubbles for the front legs. Bend and twist the legs together next to the neck.

5 Squeeze and twist a 3 cm (1¹/4 in.) bubble for the body and two 2 cm (³/4 in.) bubbles for the back legs.

6 Twist the legs together behind the body.

7 You should have a small bubble (about 2 cm (³/4 in.)) and a long piece of balloon left over to be the mouse's tail. Finish your mouse with eyes, nose and whiskers drawn in black marker pen, or use the facial feature stickers in the sticker section.

CHEESY STRAWS

⚠️ ADULT HELP NEEDED

INGREDIENTS
YOU WILL NEED:

100 g (4 oz) butter

150 g (5 oz) mature cheddar cheese, or a mixture of cheddar and parmesan

100 g (4 oz) plain flour

1 free-range egg yolk

Quick and easy to make, these delicious cheesy straws are best eaten while they are still warm from the oven!

EQUIPMENT
YOU WILL NEED:

Baking tray

Baking parchment

Grater

Large bowl

Sieve

Rolling pin

Knife

Wire rack

1 Preheat the oven to 200°C / 400°F / gas mark 6. Grease a baking tray with a little butter and cover it with a piece of baking parchment.

2 Grate the cheese.

3 Place the cheese into a bowl and sift in the flour with a sieve.

4 Cut the butter into small cubes and rub them into the mixture with your fingers. When the mixture is crumbly and the butter has almost disappeared, stir in the egg yolk.

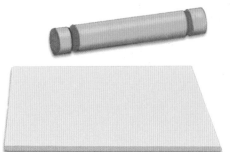

5 Next, roll the pastry into a ball. Then, dust the work surface with plenty of flour and roll out the pastry into a rough square that is 5 mm (1/5 in.) thick.

6 Cut the square into strips and transfer them onto the baking tray. Ensure that you leave a small space between each one.

7 Ask an adult to place the baking tray into a preheated oven and bake for about 7 minutes or until the cheesy straws are a pale golden brown. Transfer the cheesy straws to a wire rack and allow to cool. Yum! Yum!

JUGGLING SKILLS

The cascade, or figure-of-eight, move is the most common trick you can perform with three objects. This is the first trick most people learn when they start to juggle and will impress your friends.

1 Divide the three cubes so that one is in your left hand and two are in your right hand. Throw one of the cubes in your right hand in an arc. Start counting to keep your timing correct. Count one.

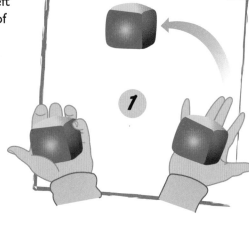

2 When the first cube has reached the top of the arc, throw up the second cube from your left hand. Count to two, by which time you should have caught the first cube in your left hand.

3 When the second cube reaches the top of the arc, throw up the third cube from your right hand and count to three, by which time you should have caught the second cube in your right hand.

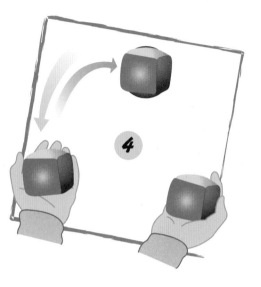

4 When the third cube reaches the top of the arc, throw up the cube from your left hand and count to four. By now, you should have caught the third cube in your left hand.

5 When the cube released from your left hand reaches the top of the arc, count to five. Continue in this pattern, throwing the cubes higher each time.

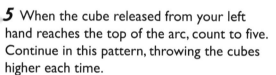

6 Practise, practise, practise! Simply think that each throw is clearing a hand to catch the next cube. Keep the pattern going for as long as possible, and then repeat until you feel really confident. Boys will be jealous!

PAPIER MÂCHÉ LADYBIRD

YOU WILL NEED:

Newspaper

Scissors

Wallpaper paste

Re-sealable container

Balloon

Sticky putty

String

Tape or glue

Paints (black, red, white)

Paintbrush

This cute ladybird model will make a great decoration for your bedroom.

1 Cut lots of strips of newspaper into 2 cm (3/4 in.) squares. These are used to cover your balloon. Make sure you prepare plenty of strips before you begin because your hands might get a bit sticky.

2 Next, ask an adult to make up 500 ml (1 pint) of wallpaper paste. Mix well and store in a re-sealable container.

3 Blow a balloon up to about 12 cm (4 3/4 in.) in length. Dip your fingers into the wallpaper paste and smooth it over the paper until it is slightly soaked (the resulting paper paste mix is called papier mâché). Once the paper is soft it can be easily laid over the balloon. Cover small areas first to check that it sticks on. You can keep the balloon steady with some sticky putty stuck to your work surface.

4 Cover the balloon with 3–4 layers of the glue-covered newspaper. Tie a piece of string around the knotted end of the balloon and hang it up to dry.

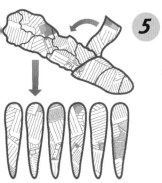

5 To make the legs, scrunch a piece of newspaper into a thin, uneven sausage shape. Cover this with a layer of papier mâché to achieve a smooth finish. Repeat step 5 until you have made six identical legs. Place these to one side to dry.

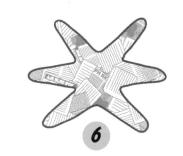

6 When all the legs have dried, bind them together with some tape to form a star shape. Cover the tape with a layer of papier mâché and then leave it to dry.

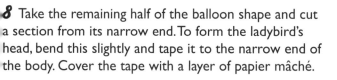

7 When the papier mâché covering the balloon is dry, pop the balloon and remove it. Form the ladybird's body by cutting the balloon-shaped papier mâché in half.

8 Take the remaining half of the balloon shape and cut a section from its narrow end. To form the ladybird's head, bend this slightly and tape it to the narrow end of the body. Cover the tape with a layer of papier mâché.

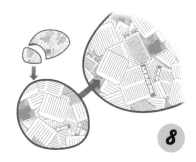

9 When all the parts have dried, stick them together, using either double-sided tape or glue. Cover all the areas where parts join with a layer of papier mâché to strengthen the whole model. Finish your model by painting in the details.

FUNKY SKITTLES

Make this fantastic game and you can challenge your friends to see who can get the highest score by knocking over these funky skittles, then stand them back up and try again! It's as much fun making them as playing the game!

1 Inflate a balloon so that it is approx 10 cm (4 in.) across and round in shape. Tear a newspaper into small squares, roughly 25 mm (1 in.) x 25 mm (1 in.), and use wallpaper paste to cover the balloon with seven layers of papier mâché.

1

2 Tie a piece of string around the neck of the balloon, as shown and hang it somewhere warn to dry.

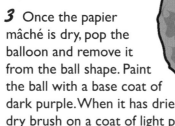

3 Once the papier mâché is dry, pop the balloon and remove it from the ball shape. Paint the ball with a base coat of dark purple. When it has dried, dry brush on a coat of light purple.

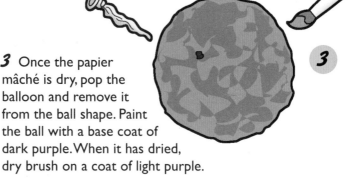

4 Find six clean, small fizzy drink bottles with lids. Pour a little paint (any colour) into one of the bottles and tightly screw on the lid. Shake the bottle until the paint completely covers the inside of it. Then, in two of the bottles pour some more paint of a different colour, and shake them. Repeat the action, using a different colour, for the last three bottles.

5 Find the funky skittles die-cut in the project component section. Push it out and then copy the body template provided five times and cut them out. Then paint each of your cute characters in a different colour. Don't forget to give them different facial expressions too!

6 Use PVA glue to fix each cardboard character onto one of the coloured bottles and you're ready to play funky skittles!

SOCK PUPPET

YOU WILL NEED:

Two ping pong balls

Paint

Paintbrushes

A black marker pen

Thin white card

Scissors

Strong PVA glue

A sock

Very quick and easy to make, this silly sock puppet will soon have your girlfriends laughing their socks off when you introduce it to them. It has a pair of brilliant bulging eyes, a bright purple nose and a big mouth — the perfect puppet playpal!

1 Find two ping pong balls. Carefully paint half of each one purple. When these are dry, add pupils and line details to each one with a black marker pen.

SOCK PUPPET TEMPLATES

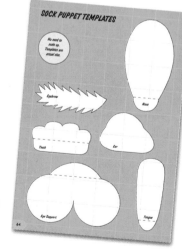

2 Copy the nose, tongue, teeth, ears, eyebrows and eye support templates (see page 64) onto thin white card. Cut these out

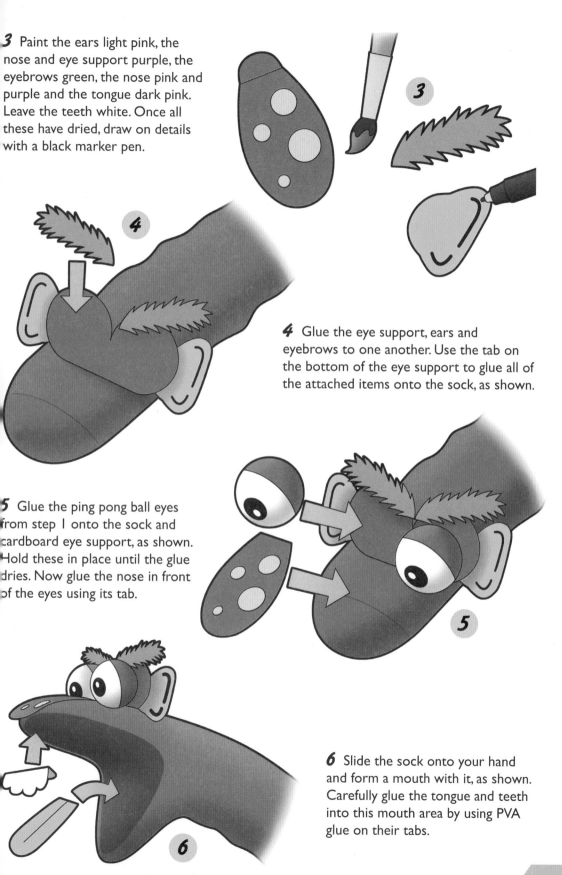

3 Paint the ears light pink, the nose and eye support purple, the eyebrows green, the nose pink and purple and the tongue dark pink. Leave the teeth white. Once all these have dried, draw on details with a black marker pen.

4 Glue the eye support, ears and eyebrows to one another. Use the tab on the bottom of the eye support to glue all of the attached items onto the sock, as shown.

5 Glue the ping pong ball eyes from step 1 onto the sock and cardboard eye support, as shown. Hold these in place until the glue dries. Now glue the nose in front of the eyes using its tab.

6 Slide the sock onto your hand and form a mouth with it, as shown. Carefully glue the tongue and teeth into this mouth area by using PVA glue on their tabs.

SOCK PUPPET TEMPLATES

No need to scale up. Templates are actual size.

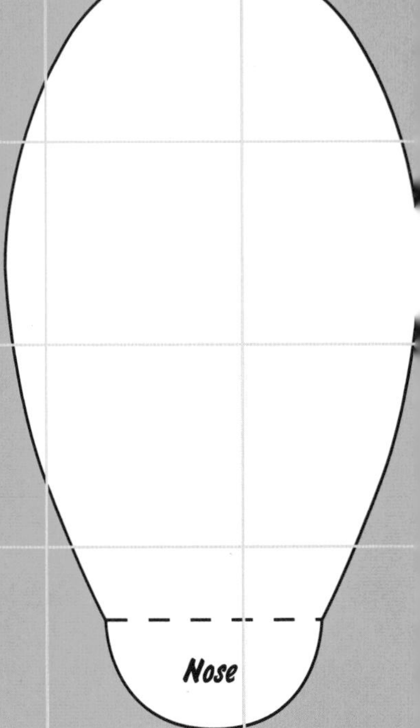

Nose

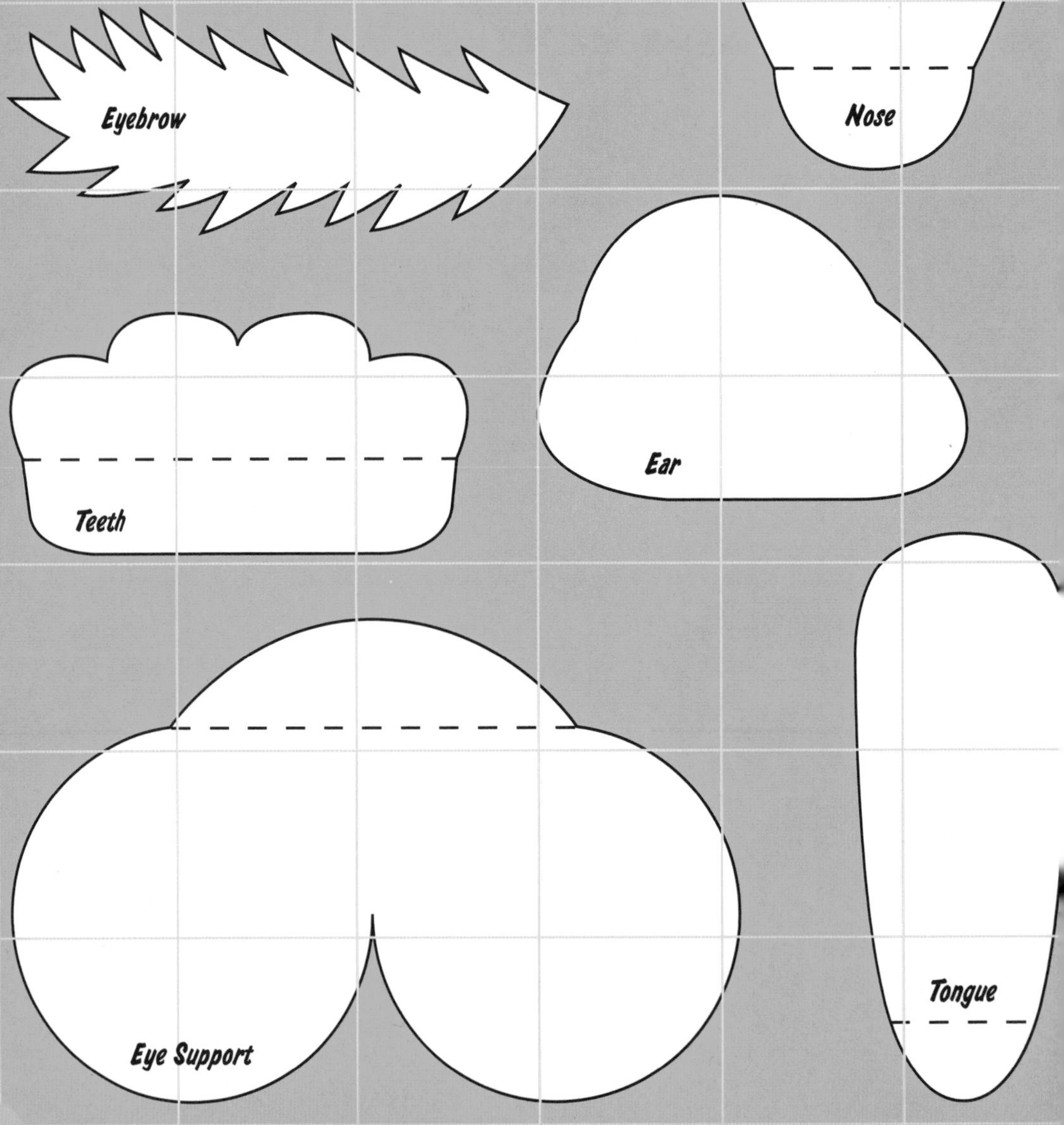

Eyebrow

Teeth

Ear

Eye Support

Tongue